Marble

GW00857951

You will ne
of fairly thin, different coloured
paints.

Find a shoe box or use a tea tray
with sides and lay your paper on
the bottom.

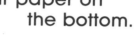

Put the marbles
into the pots
of paint.

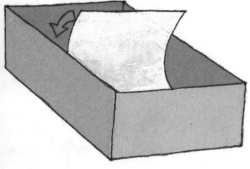

Get them out with a
straining spoon
and place them
in the box.

Gently roll the marbles
so that they leave
different coloured
trails.

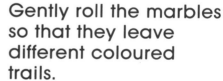

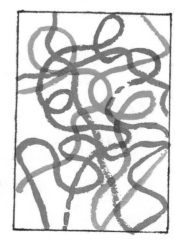

Paper folding

Dancing dolls

Fold a long sheet of thick paper backwards and forwards.

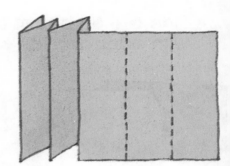

Draw half the doll against the folded edge and cut round the outline.

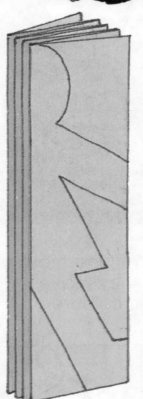

Open out your row of dolls, all holding hands, and draw faces and colour them.

In the same way you could make a row of houses or a traffic jam, for example.

Folding faces

Concertina another, thinner sheet of paper, making small folds. Tie this with wool in the middle, then open out into a circle and stick the edges together.

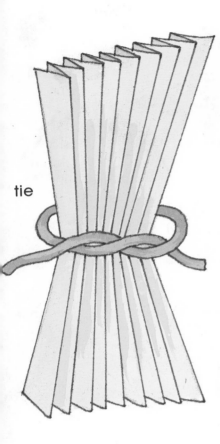

tie

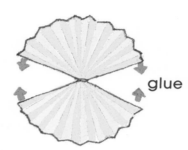

glue

Use thick felt tip pens to draw features. You could stick on paper ears, wool hair or whiskers.

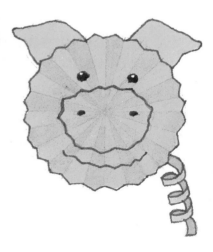

Make a curly tail by wrapping a thin strip of paper tightly round a pencil and then unwrap it and stick it to the pig.

Weaving

To make a small flowerpot holder,
make an *odd* number of holes round
the top and bottom
of a paper cup or empty
yogurt pot.

With a thick, blunt needle
(bodkin), thread thick wool
from top to bottom.

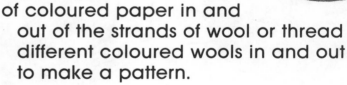

You can either weave thin strips
of coloured paper in and
out of the strands of wool or thread
different coloured wools in and out
to make a pattern.

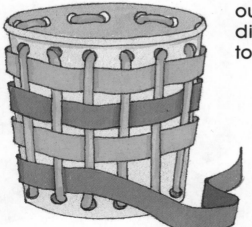

Make a bangle

To make a bangle,
carefully cut rings of plastic from a
clean, empty washing up liquid bottle.

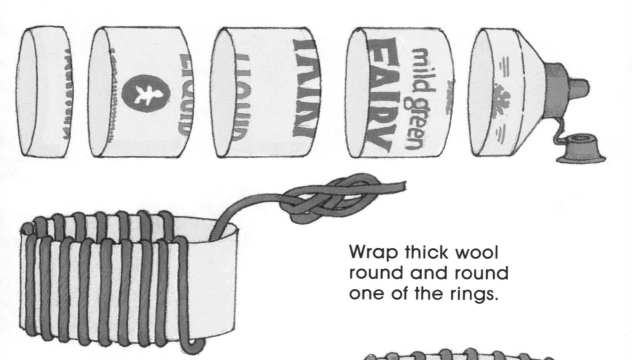

Wrap thick wool
round and round
one of the rings.

Use the bodkin to weave
other coloured wools in and out
to make your bangle.

Collecting outside

At different times of the year you can collect things to make different characters.

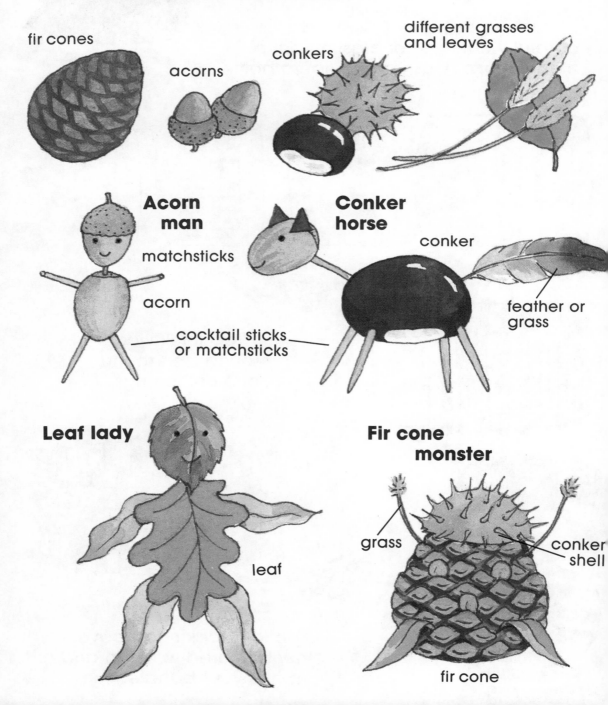

fir cones

acorns

conkers

different grasses and leaves

Acorn man

matchsticks

acorn

cocktail sticks or matchsticks

Conker horse

conker

feather or grass

Leaf lady

leaf

Fir cone monster

grass

conker shell

fir cone

Indoor garden

Next time you're out
in the garden, park,
playground or going
for a walk, collect lots of things to make a tiny garden.

Take a large paper plate or box lid and fill it with soil
or damp sand.

Then add for example:

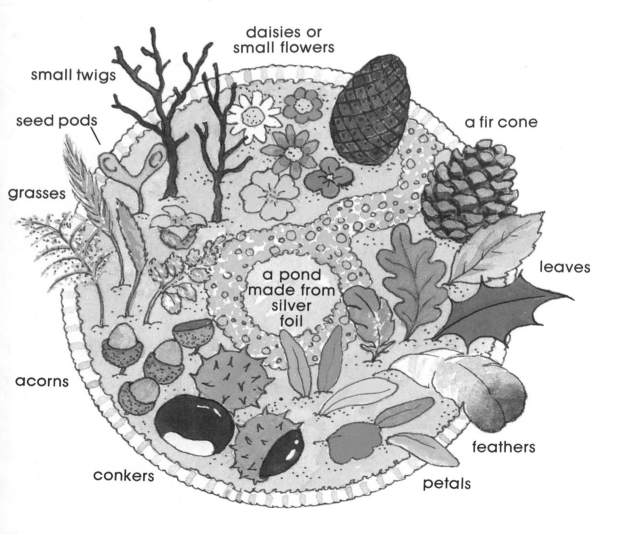

small twigs

daisies or
small flowers

seed pods

a fir cone

grasses

leaves

a pond
made from
silver
foil

acorns

conkers

feathers

petals

Weather house

Make a house from a cardboard shoe box or cereal box. Paint it and cut one door which will open.

Now make your weather people from empty cups or yogurt pots.

snow

stick paper hat to front

buttons or paper for eyes and mouth

cotton wool

sun

paper sun glasses

wind

pipe cleaners

stick on or paint a face

paper scarf

rain

paper or card umbrella

paint yellow sou'wester

paint yellow mac

Stand the house on a windowsill with all the people inside. Check the weather each day and stand the right person in the doorway.

Magic fish

Take two pieces of thin card and draw and colour a fish on one and a tank on the other.

Stick a pencil to the fish card with Sellotape.

Glue the tank card to this so that the pencil is sandwiched between the cards.

If you 'swizzle' the stick between your fingers the fish looks as though it's in its tank.

A toys' tea party

Face triangles

Spread a slice of bread with Marmite, cheese spread or peanut butter and cut into small triangles.

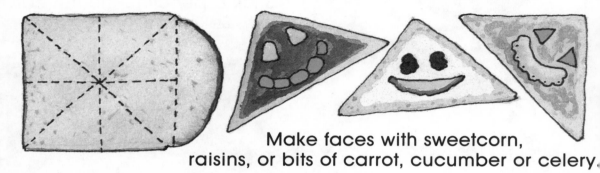

Make faces with sweetcorn, raisins, or bits of carrot, cucumber or celery.

Sweet ideas:

chocolate spread and Rice Krispies

jam and Rice Krispies

Chocolate crispies

1 Melt chocolate in a basin over hot water.

2 Stir in Rice Krispies or cornflakes or puffed wheat until covered in chocolate.

3 Put teaspoonfuls of the mixture on a baking tray and leave to harden.

Milk shake

Mash a banana or tin of fruit in a bowl.

Add milk and whisk the mixture.

You could decorate the top with chocolate chips.

Cucumber crocodile

Use cocktail sticks to attach pieces of carrot for feet and half a grape for each eye.

You can use the back of the crocodile to present pieces of cheese, sausage, apple or grapes.

Now lay the table

Here's a rhyme to help you:

A fork on the left,
A knife on the right,
A round plate
           in between.
Put a spoon across
           the top,
Eat up and leave
      your plate clean.

The peg doll family

With some old wooden pegs like this, you can make a peg doll family. They could go in your *Indoor garden*.

Draw eyes, nose and mouth on the peg.

Add wool hair.

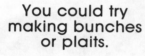
You could try making bunches or plaits.

Grandpa Peg might have cotton wool hair and a beard.

Dress your dolls with paper or pieces of material. Make arms from pipe cleaners.

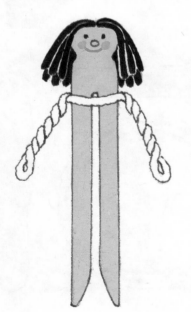

Birthday mobile

After your birthday, choose your favourite cards and cut out some of the pictures and a picture of the number that says how old you are.

Hang the pictures from a wire coat hanger using cotton thread.

You could make a Christmas mobile in the same way. Remember to save this year's Christmas cards ready for next year!

Roly poly people

Use clean, empty yogurt pots.
Save empty cotton reels.

Make a small hole in each side of the pot and push a piece of plastic drinking straw through one side, through the centre of the reel and out the other side of the pot.

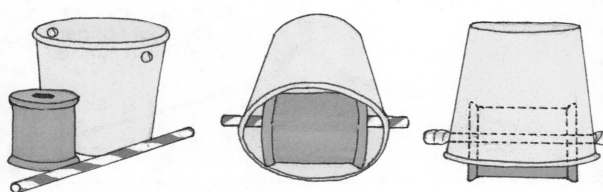

To stop the straw slipping out, fix the ends with Sellotape.

Make sure that the edge of the cotton reel is lower than the yogurt pot.

A rhyme to say

Rub a dub dub
Three men in a tub,
And who do you think
they be?
The butcher, the baker,
the candlestick maker,
Turn them out rogues
all three.

Butcher

cotton wool hair

blue and
white striped
apron

Baker

bottle top

card

paper apron

pipe cleaner arms

card loaf

Candlestick maker

wool hair

card
candle

Rolling animals

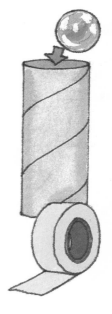

Paint and decorate
cardboard tubes.

Stick a marble inside
each tube with sticky
tape and race your
animals down a slope.

Bubble pictures

Cover your table with newspaper. Mix *thin* watery paint of different colours in empty margarine tubs. Add a little washing up liquid.

Gently blow through a straw until the bubbles are coming over the tops of the tubs.

Carefully place a piece of paper on top of the bubbles.

Your picture might look like this. When dry, you could add things to your picture using crayons or felt tips.

NOTE: You can use food colouring for this instead of paint.

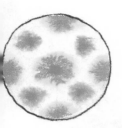

Paper dyeing

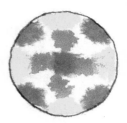

Use kitchen roll, coffee filters, blotting paper or tissues.
Fold and cut your paper in different ways.

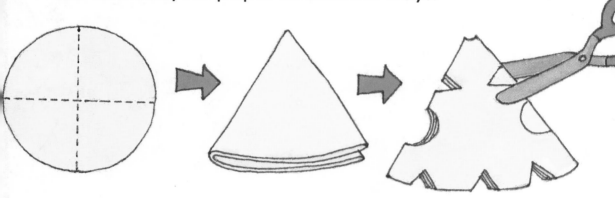

Carefully dip the corners into pots of different colours of food colouring added to water.

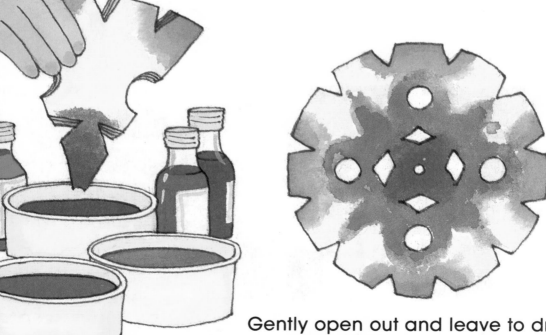

Gently open out and leave to dry.
Look at all the colours you have made.

Hunt the sheep

*Little Bo Peep has lost
        her sheep
And doesn't know
    where to find them.
Leave them alone
    and they'll come home,
Wagging their tails
        behind them.*

Trace this shape onto thin card. Make about ten sheep.

Colour the faces and legs and stick on cotton wool for the bodies.

Now play the game with a friend.

Hide each sheep in the room, e g under a chair, on the windowsill, behind a lamp.

How long does it take your partner to find all the sheep?

Snakes

For a small snake use an old stripy sock.

For a long snake cut the leg from an old pair of tights.

Stuff with crumpled pieces of newspaper and tie the end.

Stick or sew on buttons for eyes and make a long forked tongue from card or material.

You could paint coloured stripes or a pattern on your long snake.

 # Hands and feet

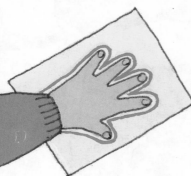

Draw round each of your hands on a piece of paper. Colour them with your crayons.

Do you know which is *left* and *right*?

Five little fingers, five little fingers,
Five little fingers – tap, tap, tap.
Point to the ceiling, point to
                    the floor
And lay them in your lap.

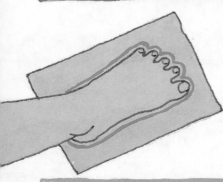

Now do the same thing, drawing round each foot.

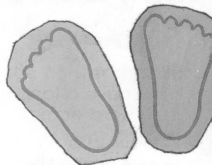

I've five little toes,
I can make them wiggle.
But when someone tickles them
It makes me giggle!

Draw round the hands and feet of everyone in your family and look at the different sizes.

Finger puppets

Find an old glove and make five round faces from thin card.

Stick a face to the end of each finger using Sellotape.

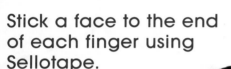

Now say this rhyme:

Tommy Thumb, Tommy Thumb,
where are you?
Here I am! Here I am! How do you do?
Peter Pointer etc.
Toby Tall etc.
Ruby Ring etc.
Baby Small etc.
Fingers all etc.
Here we are! Here we are!
How do you do?

Hanging xylophones

You can use many ordinary, everyday objects to make musical instruments.

Try these:

Use wire coat hangers and hang up card tubes of different lengths.

A collection of different plastic containers.

Different metal objects.

Tap all of these with either a wooden or metal spoon and listen to the sounds.

Splatter pictures

Cover a table with newspaper.
Mix different coloured paint, quite thin,
in empty yogurt pots.

Use old toothbrushes and dip each
one into a different colour.

Rub your finger or thumb
over the bristles and splatter
the paint onto your paper.

For Hallowe'en you
could lay ghost shapes,
cut from paper or thin
card, on your page
and splatter black
paint all over the
picture.

Remove the shapes
to leave a
spooky picture.

Matching pairs

Make your own pack of snap cards.

Look through old magazines and catalogues and cut out boots, shoes, slippers etc. Stick one of each pair onto card.

Now shuffle all the cards and play snap with a friend.

You could draw and colour your own pictures.

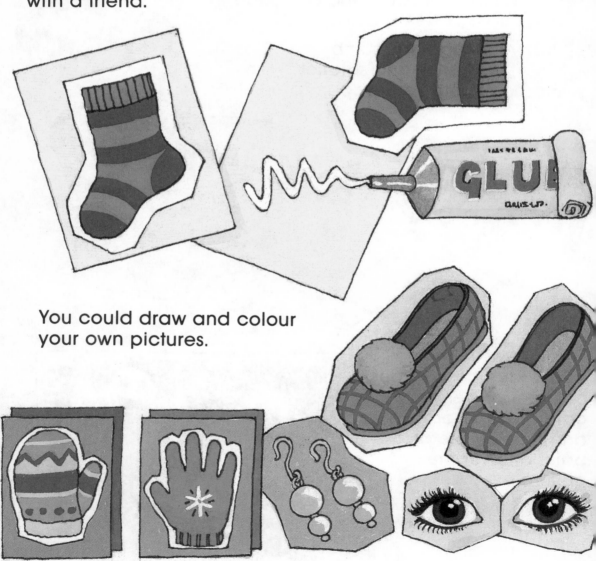